Published by Insights Press, Rochester, Minnesota.

Printed in China

Mitch Anthony's books are available at special quantity discounts. For more information, please contact
(507) 282-2723 or orders@mitchanthony.com

www.mitchanthony.com

Managing Editor: Debbie Anthony
Kid Editors: Blake Olson and Cooper Chadwick
Interior Design: Greg Wimmer
Cover Design: Greg Wimmer

ISBN: 978-0-9855000-4-7

Also by the author

The Cash in the Hat
and
The Bean is not Green

Where Did the Money Go?

by Mitch Anthony

Illustrated by Greg Wimmer

Molly looked high
and Wally looked low.
They looked at each other
and wanted to know:
"What happened to our money,
where did it all go?"

"Who can help us?
Who would know?"
They searched on Giggle.com
for a money-finding pro.

They looked everywhere;
they looked all around.
They found private "eye" (P.I.) Guy
and his Lost Money Hound.
They liked his motto:
"If it's lost, it can be found."

Molly said, "Call him!"
And Wally said, "Fast!"
With just $2 left
their money wouldn't last.

Back when they had $100
they certainly were glad.
But now, two one-dollar bills
were all that they had.

If they could find the missing fives,
they would hang on to them.
If they could find that lost ten,
they would never lose it again.

They called up P.I. Guy,
"Please come right away
and help us find our money!
Somehow it's all gone;
and we used to have plenty."

The next thing they knew,
they heard a ringing sound.
There at the door was P.I. Guy
and his Lost Money Hound.

Molly exclaimed,
"I hope it's not too late
to find all our cash."
P.I. Guy answered, "Let's first see
if you threw it in the trash."

"Threw it away?" said Wally.
"We wouldn't do that!"
"You'd be surprised," said P.I. Guy,
"to see where we find money at."

"Let Hound sniff a dollar,
so he picks up the scent.
That's how he figures out
where your money went.

He's found twenties and
he's found tens.
He's found dollar bills
and even found "Bens.""

He sniffs with his nose
and looks for the trail.
When he's found your missing money,
he'll waggle his tail.

Hound was now sniffing
and wagging that tail
as P.I. Guy stuck his hand
into the yellow garbage pail.

He pulled out a package
of melted, waxy toys,
which had a label that said,
'Lots of fun for both girls and boys!'

"Did you buy these toys
with some of your cash?
The price says $20.
How long did they last?"

"They looked so fun," said Molly,
"but they melted in the sun."
"We were going to play all day,"
chimed in Wally,
"but they faded right away!"

"And what is this?" asked P.I. Guy,
holding up a big white bag.
"Just some food," said Molly and Wally
as their heads began to sag.
"Just some burgers and some fries;
just some pop and cherry pies."

"How much for the burgers?"
asked P.I. Guy.
"How much for the fries?"
"I'm not sure," said Molly,
but I think they were five."

"Those are good clues," said P.I. Guy,
"but we must find more.
Look at Lost Money Hound;
he's headed out the door!"

They all followed him down the street,
all the way to the CoolStuff Store.

Merchanta the owner yelled,
"Get that hound out of my store!
I don't like his kind;
they only make me poor."

But the hound ran right past her
and over to a shelf,
jumping and tail wagging
at a little candy elf.
"Did you buy some of those?"
P.I. Guy asked them both.
"Oh yeah," they replied.
"They melt in your mouth!"

Merchanta then said,
"Spend all you want,
and do as you please.
Everybody knows
that money grows on trees!

Spend all you want
when you come to my store.
When your money is gone,
you just go pick some more."

"But," Molly said,
"we once had a hundred;
now we have just two.
We would have so much more
if we hadn't listened to you."

P.I. Guy informed them,
"Money doesn't grow on trees
and fall to the ground.
If it did, squirrels would be
the richest animals in town.
Merchanta says that just
to keep you coming around."

They started following Hound
as he sniffed around some more.
"Can he get our twenty," Wally asked,
and maybe even our ten?
We'll be more careful
if we get it back again."

P.I. Guy said, "He can't get it back once it's gone and spent.
His job is simply to show you where all your money went."

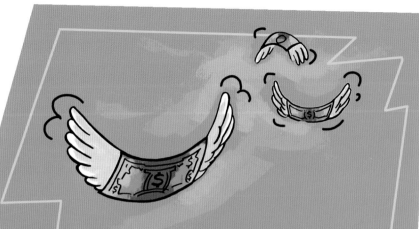

"Money grows wings
when you want to buy things."

"Money grows feet
when you crave something sweet."

"When you put it in your pocket,
it tries to run away.
You have to lock it up
and tell it where to stay."

They watched Hound chase
their two dollar bills,
but the dollars wouldn't stay!
He jumped up to catch them
as they started to fly away.

'They went back to their house
to find a little box.
They found a sturdy green one;
it even had a lock!

"Here's a little lock box;
a place to put your cash.
It can't run or fly away
when it's laying in a stash."

"Let the dollars rest in the box,
and hide the box under your socks.
You'll learn very soon
that having money rocks!"

"What do we owe you
and your money-sniffing dog?
Our missing money is gone
but the mystery is solved!"

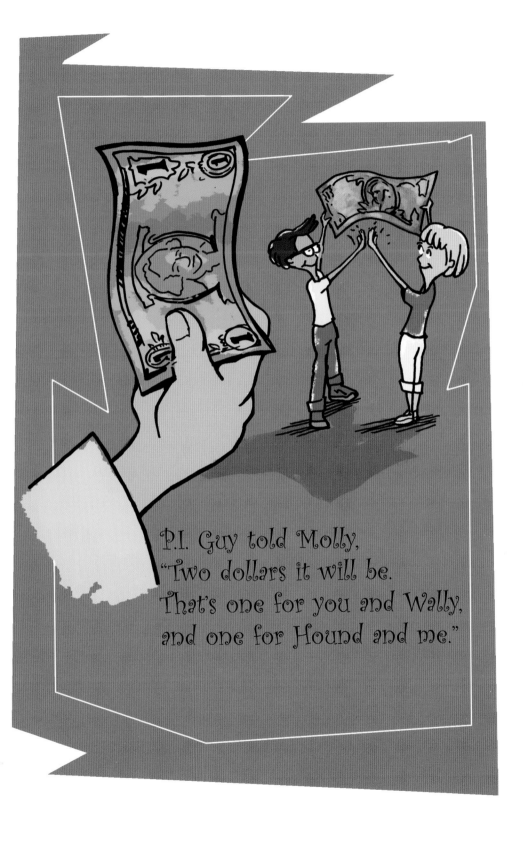

P.I. Guy told Molly,
"Two dollars it will be.
That's one for you and Wally,
and one for Hound and me."

Mitch Anthony is a leader in the education of financial services professionals and consumers about the importance of fiscal responsibility. He has been named one of the financial services industry's top "Movers & Shakers" for his efforts to bring transparency and responsibility to the industry. Mitch is the author of the popular book *The New Retirementality: Planning Your Life and Living Your Dreams…at Any Age You Want. Where Did the Money Go?* is the third book in the Financial Lit Kit. **www.mitchanthony.com**

Greg Wimmer is a Rochester, Minnesota-based graphic designer and mural artist who specializes in creating designs that get people buzzing. Many of Greg's murals have become local landmarks. View his work at **www.gregsgraphicart.com.**